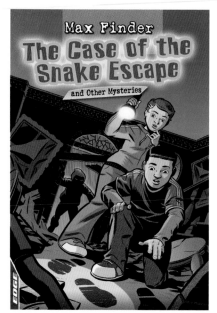

978 1 4451 0603 8

978 1 4451 0604 5

978 1 4451 0605 2

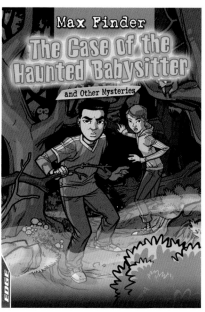

978 1 4451 0606 9

Max Finder
The Case of the
Trail Trap
and Other Mysteries

*To all Max Finder fans:
keep searching for clues and
solving mysteries.*
– LOD

This edition first published in 2011 by
Franklin Watts
338 Euston Road
London NW1 3BH

Franklin Watts Australia
Level 17/207 Kent Street
Sydney NSW 2000

Paperback original

First published in Canada by Owlkids Books Inc.

Puzzle text: Maria Birmingham
Puzzle illustrations: John Lightfoot
Comic colouring: Peter Dawes (p. 11, 17, 23, 35, 41, 47, 53, 59, 65); Chris Stone (p. 29)
Photos: Deb Yea (p. 58; skateboard courtesy of So Hip It Hurts), p. 58; Cole Thornton / fotolia
Series Design: John Lightfoot/Lightfoot Art & Design Inc.
UK edition designers: Jonathan Hair and Anna-Marie D'Cruz

Zamboni® ice resurfacing machine is a registered trademark of Frank J. Zamboni & Co., Inc.

A CIP catalogue record for this book is available from the British Library

ISBN: 978 1 4451 0604 5
Dewey classification: 741.5'971

Printed in China

Franklin Watts is a division of Hachette Children's Books,
an Hachette UK company.

www.hachette.co.uk

Max Finder
The Case of the Trail Trap

and Other Mysteries

Liam O'Donnell
Michael Cho

LONDON·SYDNEY

Max Finder
The Case of the Trail Trap
and Other Mysteries

Contents

Cases

Max Finder

The Case of the Trail Trap

and Other Mysteries

Contents

Cases

Extra Stuff

Max Finder

The Case of the Trail Trap

and Other Mysteries

HEY MYSTERY FANS!

Welcome to the **Max Finder Mysteries!** Alison and I are really excited to bring you ten of the best mysteries to hit our town of Whispering Meadows.

From the **Trail Trap** to the **Summer Sinker**, each mystery is crammed with clues, stuffed with suspects, and riddled with enough red herrings to keep you guessing until the last panel. We've done all the legwork, but solving the mystery is up to you! Read the mysteries, follow the clues and try to crack the case. All the solutions are in the back of the book. But remember: real detectives never peek.

So, fire up your mystery radar and get solving!

Max

P.S. Check out the BONUS puzzles and the artist's sketchbook, too!

Max Finder

M Y S T E R Y

The Case of the Trail Trap

Did you know the antpitta bird barks instead of sings? Max Finder here, fact collector and ace detective. It's a sunny autumn Sunday, and Alison and I are trekking through Warbler Woods on our latest case. The girl leading the way is Andrea Palgrave, our school's newest pupil and our newest client.

Leslie Chang told me you guys are the school's best detectives, so I figured you could help me out.

School's best detectives? World's greatest detectives is more like it.

Andrea is a star cross-country runner. She was out for her morning run when she stepped into a covered pit in the middle of the trail. The pit wasn't there yesterday and it certainly wasn't an accident.

I could have twisted my ankle and not been able to compete in next week's race.

That was the idea. Someone wants you out of that race, Andrea.

There are lots of footprints, and some prints from a large animal.

What's with all the yellow tape?

The tape is mine. The animal prints belong to a horse.

The kid is Andrea's little sister, Zoe. She wants to be a crime scene investigator like her mum, and even has a lab in her cellar. When Zoe heard about the trap, she rushed to the woods to collect evidence.

My plaster mould of the trap-setter's footprint is dry.

Hey, Zoe. good to have you on board.

The footprint was made by a hiking boot with a wavy tread. If we can find a boot with a matching tread, we just might find the trap-setter.

There's a riding club nearby, so hoofprints made sense. Andrea believed the footprints in Zoe's mould belonged to Jessica Peeves. Andrea had seen Jessica walking her pony along the trail that morning — right where the trap was set.

When Jessica saw me, she climbed on her pony and charged down the trail! I dived into the bushes to get out of the way.

Jessica must have known the trap was there. That's why she walked her pony around it.

If Jessica is the trap-setter, Zoe's mould will help prove it.

Jessica Peeves's dad owns half of Whispering Meadows, but Jessica acts like she owns the world. She had just finished her afternoon riding lesson when we caught up with her.

Why did you charge at Andrea on your pony?

She deserved it. We shouldn't have to share the trail with those stupid runners.

Let me put those in the boot for you, Jessica.

We had found our first suspect. But Alison thought I had lost my mind.

What's with carrying her bag, Max?

To check out her bootprint. It was wavy, just like Zoe's plaster mould.

The next day was Monday and we had to go back to school. That didn't stop the trap-setter from striking again.

Someone left a nasty note in Andrea's locker.

DROP OUT OF THE RACE, TRAITOR!

The note stirred up bad memories for Andrea. When she left Twindale, her old school, Andrea's old running buddy, a girl called Shawna Carver, called Andrea a traitor.

I didn't tell anyone except Ethan. He's my new running buddy and I knew he'd understand.

Before Andrea was around, Ethan Webster held the record for fastest runner at the school. We went looking for Ethan on the basketball court, but only found his best friend, Josh Spodek. Josh couldn't figure out why Ethan was being so nice to Andrea.

Ethan is afraid she'll beat his record in this weekend's race. He was just complaining about her yesterday during our morning basketball game.

When Ethan arrived, he was more concerned with Andrea's health than with his title as best runner at school.

Andrea and I usually run in the morning, but I wasn't feeling well yesterday. You guys have to find that trap-setter before Andrea gets hurt.

Thanks for lending me your Swiss Army knife.

Okay Mr Shoe-snooper, does Ethan have wavy treads?

Nope. Chunky. Doesn't match Zoe's plaster mould.

BASHER WUZ HERE

Andrea gave us Shawna's phone number and we called her. She denied sending the note, but agreed to talk to us anyway. We met her at Twindale.

TWINDALE PUBLIC SCHOOL

I didn't set any traps, but that's not a bad idea. With Andrea out of the race, it'll be easier for me to win.

Shoe-snoop survey says wavy tread! That matches Zoe's mould. Shawna could have been at the trail.

Okay, but how did she hide the note in Andrea's locker?

When we got back from Twindale, the phone was ringing. It was Zoe. She'd been examining the crime scene evidence in her lab.

Remember the sticks that covered the trap? They were cut neatly with a small saw.

Interesting. Thanks, Zoe.

Max, what does that knife have to do with our trap-setter?

Everything, Alison. Absolutely everything.

Do you know who tried to trip Andrea? All the clues are here. Turn to page 74 for the solution.

15

Square Search

Test your sleuthing skills and find each name hidden in these blocks.

Move from letter to letter by going up, down, across or diagonally. You can return to a letter more than once. You may not need to use every letter in each block.

1.
L	I	G
E	S	N
C	H	A

2.
D	P	S
E	O	H
J	K	X

3.
E	D	N
R	X	I
A	M	F

4.
K	R	S
D	A	O
N	W	U

5.
X	B	I
T	S	L
O	N	A

6.
H	T	B
A	S	E
N	W	R

7.
V	E	P
O	A	R
Z	L	G

8.
L	S	H
D	U	A
E	J	K

Hint: Eight of the ten following characters' names can be found in the blocks:
Alison Santos, Josh Spodek, Ethan Webster, Nanda Kanwar, Zoe Palgrave, Leslie Chang, Lukas Hajduk, Jessica Peeves, Andrea Palgrave and Max Finder.

ANSWERS ON PAGE 82

The Case of the

Model Plane Mess-up

Max Finder

MYSTERY

The Case of the Model Plane Mess-up

Did you know bats are the only mammals that can fly? Max Finder here, fact collector and ace detective. It's a cool November afternoon here in Whispering Meadows. Alison and I are out for one last bike ride before the snow arrives. But, it looks like a chill isn't the only thing in the air.

Watch out, Max!

Something is wrong. I can't control my plane!

Alex Rodriguez is president of the Flying Aces model plane club. Every Saturday, the club takes over Oakdale field. Crash landings are all part of the fun, but this crash wasn't an accident.

I just lost control of it. I don't know what happened.

Here's your answer, Alex. A couple of pieces of chewed-up gum - wildberry bubble gum, to be exact.

Someone sabotaged your plane, Alex.

18

Nicholas denied sabotaging Alex's plane. The pack of wildberry bubble gum lying beside his lunch didn't help prove his innocence.

It's my gum but I wasn't the only one chewing it – look for yourself. There are six pieces missing.

Nicholas was telling the truth. Six pieces were gone. The pieces of gum that downed Alex's plane definitely came from this pack.

Did everyone take a piece of gum?

Everyone except Katlyn. She doesn't like wildberry gum. Alex took her piece, so I guess he got two pieces.

Nicholas said he had finished his piece of gum and tossed it in the bin. He had the blue tongue to prove it.

Alex teases Crystal because she's still learning to fly. She was so mad at him last week that she tried to ride over his plane with her bike.

Meanwhile, on the other side of the field things were heating up.

Get lost, Stuart! I don't need your help. I bet you're the one who wrecked my plane.

How did such a jerk become club president?

Morse Message

Alex sent Max and Alison a note. The problem is he wrote it in Morse code. **What does the note say?**

TIP: Morse code is written with a slash (/) between letters and a double slash (//) between words.

Morse code symbols

A .-	J .---	S ...
B -...	K -.-	T -
C -.-.	L .-..	U ..-
D -..	M --	V ...-
E .	N -.	W .--
F ..-.	O ---	X -..-
G --.	P .--.	Y -.--
H	Q --.-	Z --..
I ..	R .-.	

ANSWER ON PAGE 82

Lucky Skates

The Case of the Lucky Skates

Max Finder

MYSTERY

Did you know ice hockey pucks are frozen so they won't bounce during games? Max Finder here, ace detective and reluctant ice hockey fan. It's just before the playoff game between the Meadows Minotaurs and the Timber Creek Titans. Alison dragged me along to cheer for the Minotaurs, her brother's team.

I know you'd rather be reading a book, Max, but try to look excited. Roll up your sleeves and no one will know you're wearing my dad's shirt.

We were on our way to the stands when Tony DeMatteo, the star of the Minotaurs, came running from the changing room.

Max! Alison! Somebody stole my skates!

Tony is set to beat the record for the most goals scored in a season. A few months ago, Dimitri Kozlov, the NHL* hockey star, signed Tony's ice skates.

They're old ice skates, but since the Russian rocket signed them, I've been a scoring machine! I'll need them if I'm going to beat that record and win the playoff game.

Tony forgets that ice hockey is a team sport. His ego is the size of an NHL player's pay cheque. But he looked desperate, and so did Alison. I guess the thought of Tony missing out on the playoff game was too much for her.

We'll find those skates, Tony.

Start from the beginning and tell us what happened.

*National Hockey League (of North America)

I arrived early to grab lunch before the game. I sat with right winger Lorrisa Swart. Her whole family plays hockey. Basher McGintley was there, too. Basher plays in defence, but I think he wishes he could score more goals.

I'm going to the toilet. Can you watch my bag, Lorrisa?

Sure thing, Tony.

Lorrisa didn't do a good job of watching my bag. When I got back she was gone. So was Basher. The two Titans players were still there and they were up to something.

Hey there, Mighty Minotaur!

Hope your skates are extra lucky today. You're going to need them!

I like to settle scores on the ice, so I ignored the Titan losers and dropped off my bag in the changing room. I didn't have time to see if they took my skates, because Coach Coleman wanted the team out in the stands to go over our strategy.

Remember to work the zone defence, pass the puck and keep your heads up.

Back in the changing room, I checked my bag and my skates were gone!

Somebody doesn't want you playing in this game...

...or the Minotaurs winning the finals.

Tony went back to the changing room, and Alison and I went to the snack bar. Doug Chang was cleaning up after the pre-game rush. I asked if he'd seen anything strange.

Lorrisa knocked over that rubbish bin with her blue ice hockey bag. That thing was so big she couldn't carry it! She just dragged it across the floor.

On the floor near the girls' toilet, we turned up an important clue.

It's a blade guard from a hockey skate.

Tony D.

It was pretty easy to see who the guard belonged to. I checked inside the bin, but it was empty. The bag had been changed.

I talked to the arena caretaker while Alison checked out the girls' toilet. She ran into Nanda Kanwar, who plays goalie and was all geared up for the game.

I hear Simon Swart isn't happy about Tony trying to break his high-score record. Simon has held that record for five years and wants to play in the NHL.

I found the caretaker, Gary, behind the hockey rink. Gary drives the Zamboni® ice resurfacing machine that cleans the ice. He didn't see any skates in the rubbish.

But I did see a short guy with glasses snooping around the Minotaurs' changing room while the whole team was sitting in the stands. He was wearing a Titans jacket, so I told him to get lost.

Coach's Corner

Coach Coleman is filling in the Meadows Minotaurs' scoring chart. **Use the clues to find out who is the leading scorer on the team.**

Meadows Minotaurs

Player	Number	Position	Goals
Tony DeMatteo	17	Left Wing	--
Basher McGintley	6	Defence	3
Lorissa Swart	12	Right Wing	--
Marcus Santos	8	Left Wing	9
Alex Rodriguez	21	Defence	--
Leslie Chang	3	Centre	--
Josh Spodek	18	Defence	--
Layne Jennings	15	Defence	10
Nicholas Musicco	7	Right Wing	--
Nanda Kanwar	31	Goalie	0

Clues:
- Leslie has scored twice as many goals as Lorrisa.
- Lorrisa has scored in just two games, but got a hat trick (three goals) each time.
- Nicholas has five more goals than Layne, but two fewer than Alex.
- Josh has scored half as many goals as Leslie.
- Tony has scored twice as many goals as Alex.

ANSWER ON PAGE 82

The Case of the Angry Anchorman

Max Finder

MYSTERY

Did you know the world's hairiest donkey is the Poitou from France? Max Finder here, fact collector and ace detective. My class is at our local TV station to present the money we raised for their children's charity. That woman talking to us works at the station. She is also my mum.

Welcome to CKWM! And a special welcome to my son. I'll try not to embarrass you, Max.

Too late for that!

GREEN ROOM

Jan 09/07
CKWM Children's Fund $510.00
Five hundred and ten —00/00

7 (

Arrgh!

Ouch!

A few seconds later, I wasn't the only one in an embarrassing situation.

The guy covered in plant dirt is Bull O'Wiley, CKWM's news anchor and big boss at the station. The kid is Kyle Kressman. He loves practical jokes, but this one had accident written all over it.

Watch where you're standing, you little twerp!

That's enough, Kyle!

Watch where you're walking!

Our teacher, Mr Reed, chewed Kyle out for tripping Bull. Kyle sulked off to the toilet and stayed there.

GREEN ROOM

Where have you been, Ursula? Have you seen Kyle?

What? No. I was talking to Deb, the make-up artist.

Ursula's father also worked at the station, so she knew a lot of the adults here. The waiting around was making us thirsty, so we joined her at the snack table.

I spilled some juice. The table could be sticky.

Doesn't feel sticky to me.

That's because she used half a forest's worth of napkins.

Max, Alison, we have a problem.

We followed Mum to Bull O'Wiley's dressing room. He was there, but his hair wasn't.

Someone stole Mr O'Wiley's wig, er, his hair.

Someone? It wasn't someone. It was one of those kids! I can't go on TV looking like a boiled egg.

It was my mum's bright idea to bring us to the station, but now it looked like it was backfiring.

Listen kid, find my hair before five o'clock or your mum will work on the late news until you graduate!

There he is!

There you are! You're supposed to stay in the green room!

What were you doing in there, Kyle?

Payback for Bull O'Wiley. Nobody gets me in trouble. Want some gum?

The news starts in five minutes, little detectives. Where's my hair?

Start practising your lines, Mr O'Wiley. I know where your wig is.

And the thief is in this room.

Do you know who stole Bull O'Wiley's hair and where it's hidden? All the clues are here. Turn to page 76 for the answer.

Newscast Mad Lib

What's in the news?
Ask a friend to write out these news stories, filling in the text in brackets. Then read the completed stories out aloud.

Welcome to tonight's news.
I'm [your name]. In our top story, the city of [type of cheese] was in chaos today after a [wild animal] jumped out of a [kitchen appliance] and ran up and down the street in a [article of clothing]. Traffic came to a standstill, and a passerby cried out for [name of a superhero]. The police asked [famous singer] to sing [kids' song] to calm everybody down. Then they instructed the crowds to head for [far-off country]. The city is finally as quiet as a [musical instrument] this evening.

Now for the sport: the [type of dog] beat the [type of fish] today thanks to the efforts of [a friend's mum]. And the [exotic animal] beat the [fruit] in added time. [Name of family pet] has decided to retire from [extreme sport] to take up [kind of dance]. Finally, [famous football star] will be travelling to [your school] tomorrow night to teach kids all about [favourite video game] and [type of junk food].

And in weather, for the first time in [big number] years, a [vegetable] fell from the sky during a freak storm. Luckily, [television character] gathered it up and made [your favourite meal] out of it. For tomorrow, it looks like it'll be raining cats and [type of bug]. So, be sure to carry a [piece of sports equipment] with you. That's tonight's news. Good night, and remember to keep your [body part] in your pocket.

The Case of the

Missing Manga

The Case of the Missing Manga

Max Finder
MYSTERY

Max Finder here, fact collector, ace detective, and very late manga fan.

Kengo Takahashi, one of my favorite artists, is launching his new manga series at the comic shop.

Max! You're an hour late. Where have you been?

I got sucked into the final level of *World Warlordz* and lost track of time.

Did I miss much?

Just everything.

Lucky for you I took some pics.

Our friend, Sarah Khadda, won an autographed page from Takahashi's new series.

Sarah introduced her comic-loving friend, Crystal Diallo, to Takahashi.

While Crystal was getting a headband for her hair, Sarah got drawing tips.

Alison snapped one last photo of Crystal and Sarah with Takahashi.

I had missed most of the signing, but I didn't want to miss seeing Sarah's prize.

Hey Sarah, let's have a look at your manga page.

Sure, Max. It's right here in my - sketchbook?

This isn't mine! It's gone! Someone stole my prize!

I put the manga page inside my sketchbook to keep it safe. Then I put it in my bag.

You and Crystal left your bags by the spinner rack while you were talking to Takahashi.

Someone must have swapped sketchbooks while Alison was taking photos of you.

Okay, but whose sketchbook is that?

It's mine! How'd you get it?

Jake! Wait!

No time to talk, Max! My ride is here.

I just want to ask you some questions!

Why? So, you can pin this on me? No way, Max.

VRRRMM

Have fun playing detective, Max!

Jake Granger was a huge Takahashi fan and a prime suspect. He was the key to solving this case.

Meanwhile, Alison wasn't having much luck with Travis, the comic shop assistant.

All I saw was a bunch of kids looking at comics.

I don't trust Travis. He was hanging around the spinner rack. And he sells anime stuff on the web.

I bet he could get a good price for your manga page.

We caught a bus home and that gave us a chance to talk to Crystal.

Did you see anyone near Sarah's bag?

No. I was getting my photos taken with Sarah and Takahashi the whole time.

DINGG!

We were going to work on our comic this afternoon.

I saw her mum earlier. She's off work today.

This is my stop. I'll see you tomorrow, Sarah.

We can do that at school. I've got to babysit my brother until my mum gets back from work.

The next day at school, we dropped by the manga club. Crystal and Sarah's comic was going to be in the school paper and they were rushing to get it finished.

We both drew covers. We were going to use mine, but it was in my sketchbook.

I can't wait for the whole school to see my cover!

Hey guys, check out the new cover for our comic.

PIXIE PATROL
BY CRYSTAL DIALLO AND SARAH KHADDA

Nowhere to run now, Jake. Start talking.

I'm innocent, Max. I left my sketchbook on my bag near the rack. Then I saw Sarah pulling it out of her bag.

After school we went to Alison's and checked out Travis's website.

We've searched the whole site and there's no listing of the manga page.

Maybe Travis didn't steal it.

TRAVIS'S ANIME TRADING POST
NEW!

Maybe he doesn't need to post it to sell it. I bet he's got a list of interested buyers.

He'd just have to send an email and wait for someone to make him an offer.

So, searching on the computer was a waste of time.

CLIK.

Maybe not. I think the answer to this mystery is in Alison's photos.

Do you know who stole Sarah's sketchbook? All the clues are here. Turn to page 76 for the solution.

Decode It

This page from Sarah's sketchbook is packed full of pictograms.
Can you decipher the meaning of each one?

①
```
     r
T  world  i
     p
```

②
Wish
star

③
secret
secret
secret

④
h o r s i n g (arranged in a circle)

⑤
mo onceon

⑥
yrotcivyrotciv

⑦
HE
NOW RE

⑧
Dutch
Dutch

⑨
shopshopshopshop
u

⑩
NV

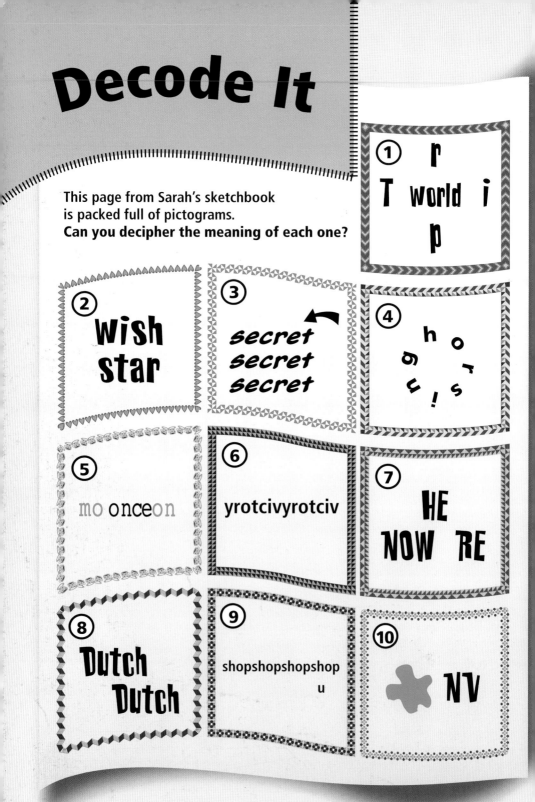

ANSWERS ON PAGE 82

The Case of the Elvis Prankster

Max Finder
MYSTERY

Did you know that the Basenji breed of dog yodels instead of barks? Max Finder here, fact collector and ace detective. Alison and I are at the Pilton Meadows Hotel to meet Alison's older brother, Marcus.

Looking good, Marcus! How's the new job?

SPECIAL EVENTS
ELVIS-CON 2005
GRAND BALLROOM

MEADOWS DOG SHOW
JUNIOR BALLROOM

What's with all the dogs and rock 'n' rollers?

There's a dog show and an Elvis convention this weekend. It's been crazy!

Elvis Presley may have been the king of rock 'n' roll, but Nicole Pilton was not a fan. Nicole's father owned the hotel. She was helping organise the dog show.

Marcus, these Elvis dorks have been up to their lame tricks again!

JUNIOR BALLROOM

MEADOWS DOG SHOW

Deep-fried peanut butter sandwiches might have been Elvis's favourite snack, but they are not for dogs! One more prank and Daddy will kick every Elvis out of this hotel.

Nicole, we didn't do it!

Looks like someone is trying to shut down the Elvis convention. But why?

The guys claiming innocence were Alvin Potter and Eric Brady. Eric's competing in the 16-and-under Elvis Impersonator contest. Alvin is the reigning champ, but this year he is 17 and too old to compete.

The room should be empty, but there's a vintage Elvis cape covered in red hair. No true Elvis fan would let it get so dirty.

Dish soap, pink food coloring, and mini-wigs?

Outside in the hallway, it looked like Nicole and Alvin weren't enemies after all.

432

431

DOG SHOW HEADQUARTERS PLEASE KNOCK

I bet you're the Elvis prankster. If tonight's show gets cancelled you'd still get to be the Elvis champ.

Me?! You and Tinkerbell are mad because your dad gave the Elvises the grand ballroom.

Hey, Nicole. Has your dad kicked out the Elvises yet?

Give it a rest, Chester. Now leave me alone. Tinkerbell needs her bath before tonight's big show.

Next door, I could hear running water. But that wasn't what worried me.

CLICK!

Someone's coming! Hide!

Photo Play

This puzzle is doggone fun! Only three identical dog photos appear in all three boxes. **Can you find them?**

ANSWER ON PAGE 82

The Case of the Gander River Grudge

Max Finder

MYSTERY

Did you know that geese use ten different sounds to talk to each other? Max Finder here, fact collector and ace detective. It's Earth Day, and our class is cleaning up the banks of the Gander River in Gander Park.

This rubbish is smellier than my mum's cabbage soup!

Those Canada Geese look sick.

Not again!

The river isn't the only thing that needs our help.

Becca Bastedo was our group leader for the Earth Day clean-up. She also helps out at the local animal shelter.

In the last week, we've found several sick geese near here. We think somebody is making them ill on purpose.

Becca took the geese to the animal shelter while we checked out the crime scene.

Who would want to do this to harmless geese?

Whoever it is, we'd better stop them before they try again.

These beans are scattered everywhere. They could be coated with a chemical that's making the geese sick.

That night, we staked out the river to see if we could catch the bean bandit in action. We spotted Zack across the river at the golf course. He seemed to be working on the grass.

SPUT SPUT

Here come Josh and his dad. That truck is so loud, it will probably scare all the fish away.

Let's follow them when they go down to fish.

Suddenly a figure burst out of the bushes and sent me flying.

SMAK!

Whoa!

This way. Be careful. These rocks are slippery.

HRRMMMM

Pain shot through my leg. A low hum droned in my ears, but it wasn't from my fall. I'd heard that hum before.

Max, are you all right?

I think I broke my leg! But I solved the case!

AAAAH

THUNK!!

MAX!!

Do you know who is making the geese sick? All the clues are here. Turn to page 78 to find out.

Cast Code

Max helped solve the mystery at Gander River, but he ended up with a broken leg. Alison has signed his cast with this secret message. She's using numbers to represent the letters of the alphabet, so that 1 = A and 26 = Z.
Can you crack her code?

13 1 24'

13 1 24 '   1 2 15 21 20   20 8 5   2 18 15 11 5 14

20 15 15   2 1 4   1 2 15 21 20   20 8 5   2 18 15 11 5 14   23 15 18 11   3 1 14

2 15 14 5 .   9   7 21 5 19 19   4 5 20 5 3 20 9 22 5   23 15 18 11   3 1 14

2 5   1   16 1 9 14   9 14   20 8 5   12 5 7   19 15 13 5 20 9 13 5 19

8 1 !   8 1 !

1 12 9 19 15 14

18 3 26 10 6 5 '

13 22   9 16   23 12 5 5 16 .   11 25 6 10 22

18 9 22   11 25 22   19 9 22 18 2 10   14 25 22 5

16 6 12   9 22   18   21 22 11 22 20 11 26 13 22

22 15 11   9 18 6   9 21 26 5 18 26 9 22 !

4 18 15

The Case of the

Nosy Neighbour

Max Finder MYSTERY

The Case of the Nosy Neighbour

Did you know that babies have more than 300 bones in their bodies, but adults only have 206? Max Finder here, fact collector and ace detective. Last month I broke my leg, so I'm itching to get my cast off and to find a new mystery.

Binoculars are not for snooping on your neighbours, Max!

Garden watching is way more fun than birdwatching.

Every garden holds a story. Mrs Briggs's puppy lift saved her from climbing the stairs to let her dog, Peaches, out anytime he wanted, which was every 10 minutes.

Russell Wagner's parents were going away for the weekend, and it didn't look like he'd miss them one bit.

Nobody likes a nosy neighbour, Max. Remember, they know where you live, too.

Later that night...

KRASH!

What was that?

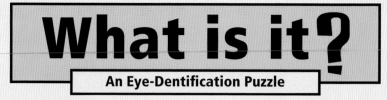

What is it?

An Eye-Dentification Puzzle

Max and his broken leg have been stuck in his room for days.
Can you work out what objects he's spotted out of
the window with his binoculars?

ANSWERS ON PAGE 83

The Case of the

Reflection Detection

Max Finder

MYSTERY

The Case of the Reflection Detection

Did you know that football was played in Japan 3,000 years ago? Max Finder here, fact collector, ace detective, and sidelined football player. The cast came off my leg last week, but I still can't play in the season finals against the Twindale Tornadoes.

I know I went to Twindale last year, Max, but I want the Meadows Meteors to win!

That's going to be tough, Zoe, if Basher doesn't stop this shot.

POOMP!

Gah! My eyes!

YAAY!

SWISH!

Something flashed in my eyes. It blinded me!

At half-time our team was down by a goal. We filled in Zoe's sister, Andrea, and Alison with our investigation so far.

Kate's had a grudge against the football team since she had to quit to improve her grades.

My last year at Twindale I had Mr Huckle for Science. He taught us how mirrors reflect light.

Not long into the second half...

Ahh!

This time it came from that snack bar!

Let's go!

The busy snack bar was the perfect place for the mirror flasher to hide out.

SNACK BAR

You'd need to be high up to get a clear shot of the football pitch from here.

I don't see the mirror flasher around here.

Exactly. Get back in the game, Alison. I know who is blinding the players.

Who is blinding the football players? Turn to page 79 to find out.

Forensics Quiz

Test your C.S.I. (that's crime scene investigation) skills with the true or false questions below. Write your answers on a separate piece of paper.

TRUE or FALSE

1. There are three main types of fingerprint. They're called arch, loop and globular.

2. Detectives and forensic scientists can use toe prints or lip prints to identify someone.

3. The fingerprint brush that detectives use to dust for prints may be made from squirrel hair.

4. To lift hair and fibres from surfaces, detectives often use a comb.

5. Detectives often make a cast, or mould, of a footprint to preserve their find, in case they need it later.

6. By examining a strand of hair, scientists can help a detective determine if the person was male or female.

7. Detectives may use a special vacuum cleaner to suck up evidence at a crime scene.

8. By looking closely at an imprint made by a foot inside a shoe, detectives can match it to the actual foot.

9. At crime scenes, investigators bring their own super-bright lights so they don't miss any clues.

10. By examining someone's handwriting, detectives can figure out whether the person is left-handed or right-handed.

ANSWERS ON PAGE 83

The Case of the

Summer Sinker

The Case of the
Summer Sinker

Max Finder
MYSTERY

It says they found a red baseball cap in a boat with "Danny Santos" written inside it. That's your grandfather's name!

He hates being called Danny. Besides, anyone could have planted that hat. Grandpa isn't the boat sinker! We gotta clear his name, Max.

Everyone knows your Grandpa did it, Alison. The old man is a joke around here.

I stopped Alison from covering Cory in sticky cola in time to see his grandfather approaching. He was talking to Amanda's grandpa. They were old buddies and were having a good laugh at Grandpa Santos.

Good day for a sail, Eugene. I wish I'd brought my boat.

Lucky you didn't, Warren. Never let Danny "the sinker" Santos near a boat!

Alison was determined to clear her grandfather's name. After the barbecue, we plunged into our investigation.

Tell you about the Boat Sinker? Sorry, kids. That's ancient history.

It may have been the end of the story for Grandpa Santos, but for Alison and me, the mystery was just getting started.

The next day, we headed to the library. The boat sinkings made all the papers around Trout Lake that summer. The sinker struck during the annual fireworks show.

The entire town was at the beach watching the fireworks.

Margaret Kim, the librarian, is friends with Grandpa Santos. She remembered the boat sinkings — and that red baseball cap.

One witness saw a skinny kid in a red baseball cap at the marina during the fireworks.

Your grandpa lost that cap before the sinking. I saw the whole thing.

A week before the sinkings, I was at the marina. Dan was visiting his friend Eugene, who worked there with Warren. Warren's dad owned the marina and the restaurant in town.

Dan, we're off to the beach while my dad is at lunch.

Be a pal, Danny. Watch the boats while we're gone!

Dan would do anything to avoid swimming. He hated taking off his shirt because he felt chubby. But when the wind picked up, Dan saved the boats.

Where the heck are Warren and Eugene?

They went swimming, Sir!

Mr Klein fired Eugene and made Warren wash the dishes in his restaurant. Both boys blamed Dan for telling on them.

After lunch, we paid a visit to Eugene. He and Warren had a motive, but did they have an alibi? We asked him where he was when the boat sinker struck.

I remember it well. I was with Margaret and Warren on the beach watching the fireworks.

I watched the whole show. Warren had to work in the kitchen, and your grandfather showed up just as the fireworks were ending.

Eugene, you goof. You told me you'd all be at your cabin!

That's rubbish, Danny! My cabin is at the far end of the lake. You can't see the fireworks from there.

Storytelling really took it out of Eugene. After a few questions, he snored like we weren't even there. A good detective never turns down the chance to snoop, so we snuck into Eugene's cabin. Our snooping paid off.

Hey! What are you guys doing?

Your grandpa and Eugene were best friends, weren't they?

It was only Amanda. She had dropped by to visit her grandfather, but didn't mind us snooping. Her grandfather was a total pack rat, but yesterday he suddenly decided to throw out some old papers.

Eugene, I can't go swimming tomorrow. I'm stuck washing dishes, thanks to that rat fink, Dan Santos. But I'm working on a plan to get back at him!

Warren

I found this in the pile. Think it'll help with your case? I told Grandpa all about your investigation.

Wow. Warren was really mad at my Grandpa.

Our next stop was the crime scene — the marina. Though he was a suspect, Warren seemed happy to see us. We couldn't say the same for Cory.

KLEIN'S MARINA
BOAT STORAGE AND RENTALS
RATES

Watch out! Here comes the next-generation Santos Sinker!

Put a cork in it, Cory.

Postcard Scramble

Cory is spending his summer holiday at Trout Lake. He's been sending postcards to his friend, Jeff Bean, telling him about all the fun he's having. **Can you put the postcards in the correct order?**

a

Hey Jeff,
Wakeboarding rules. I'm a natural. Amanda showed me "the big rock" on the other side of the lake. She says we're going to jump off it soon. It's scary-high. Wish me luck.
Your pal,
Cory

Beautiful Trout
Catch the 'big one'

Jeff
311 T
Norwi,
NR1 3A

b

Hey Jeff,
I just arrived but so far Trout Lake is wicked. First thing I want to try is wakeboarding. Fishing is supposed to be good, too. I've got all summer to try my luck.
Your pal,
Cory

Beautiful Trout Lake
Catch the 'big one'

51

Jeff Bean
311 Turner St
Norwich, Norfol
NR1 3AJ

c

Hey Jeff,
We had a huge bonfire last night. It was cool to hang out by the fire. Especially because there were bats swooping down at our heads. I can't believe summer's almost over.
Your pal,
Cory

Beautiful Trout Lake
Catch the 'big one'

Jeff Bean
311 Turner
Norwich,
NR1 3A

d

Hey Jeff,
We finally jumped off "the big rock" today. Man, it was scary – but amazing. And then I actually found my sunglasses. They washed up on shore. Can you believe that? The best day yet!
Your pal,
Cory

Beautiful Trout Lake
Catch the 'big one'

Jeff Bean
311 Turner St
Nor
rfol

e

Hey Jeff,
Went fishing today. Pretty boring after wakeboarding. I didn't catch a thing. And, I dropped my sunglasses in the lake. They're gone for good.
Your pal,
Cory

Je
311
Nor
NR1

f

Hey Jeff,
Gave the fishing thing another chance. I left my sunglasses at the cabin this time... just in case! Still no trout. Having a bonfire tomorrow. I wish you could be here!
Your pal,
Cory

Beautiful Trout Lake
Catch the 'big one'

51

Jeff Bean
311 Turner St
Norwich, Norfolk
NR1 3AJ

ANSWER ON PAGE 83

Who? What? When? Where? How? Why?

Case Solutions

The Case of the Trail Trap

(page 11)

Who made the trap to trip Andrea?
• **Ethan Webster.** Ethan was scared of losing his spot as the school's top cross-country runner. So he sawed sticks with Josh's Swiss Army knife to make a trap that would hurt Andrea and put her out of the upcoming race.

How did Max solve the case?
• Ethan was the only person at school who knew that Shawna had called Andrea a traitor.
• Max and Alison saw Ethan return the Swiss Army knife to Josh.
• Ethan said he was too ill to go running with Andrea on the morning she found the trap. But Josh said that he and Ethan had played basketball "yesterday morning" – the same day Andrea found the trap.
• Josh also told the detectives that Ethan complained about Andrea.
• Further study of Zoe's footprint mould showed it was made from Jessica's riding boot. She walked around the trap because her pony sensed something was wrong on the trail and wouldn't walk forward. The pony knew the trap was there even if Jessica didn't!

Conclusion
When faced with the evidence, Ethan confessed to setting the trap. As a punishment, he wasn't allowed to run in the weekend's big race. Andrea won the race and easily beat Ethan's best time.

The Case of the Model Plane Mess-up

(page 17)

Who crashed Alex's plane?
• **Katlyn Rodriguez.** Katlyn didn't want to spend her Saturday afternoon flying model planes, so she took Alex's pieces of wildberry gum from his coat pocket, chewed them, and wedged them into the wing of the plane. Katlyn didn't know much about planes, but she hoped that would be enough to ground Alex for the day and get her to the cinema.

How did Alison solve the case?
• Although she denied chewing any of the wildberry gum, Katlyn had a blue tongue. (She stuck it out when they were all walking home.)
• Crystal and Katlyn helped prepare Alex's plane for flight, but Crystal was still chewing her piece of gum after the crash. She blew a bubble when Stuart was looking at the damaged wing.
• Nicholas had chewed his gum but hadn't spoken to Alex for a month, so he didn't get near enough to the plane to sabotage it.

How? Why? Where?

- Stuart hadn't even chewed his gum when Max and Alison spoke to him.
- Alison spotted Katlyn and Alex at the cinema. That reminded Alison that Katlyn didn't want to go flying in the first place. She wanted to see a movie instead.

Conclusion
Max and Alison confronted Katlyn just before Alex bought the movie tickets. Katlyn confessed to wedging gum into the wing of her brother's plane and apologised. Instead of spending the money on a movie, Katlyn and Alex bought new parts for the crashed plane. They spent the afternoon fixing the plane and getting it ready for one last flight before the winter snows arrived.

The Case of the Lucky Skates
(page 23)

Who stole Tony's skates?
- **Lorrisa Swart.** She didn't want Tony to beat her brother Simon's high-scoring record. So she took Tony's lucky skates, knowing it would make him miss the game.

Where were the lucky skates hidden?
- Behind the arena, in the snow pile created by the Zamboni®.

How did Alison solve the case?
- Doug Chang said Lorrisa knocked over the rubbish bin with a blue hockey bag. But Alison saw Basher looking through Lorrisa's green bag. The blue bag was Tony's. (Basher was looking for skate laces.)
- Lorrisa hid in the girls' toilet to take Tony's skates from his bag. Tony's skate guard fell from the bag when Lorrisa knocked over the bin on her way into the toilet.
- Alison was suspicious about the open toilet window. As she talked to Max from the window, she noticed the freshly dumped snow directly below her.
- Lorrisa threw Tony's skates out of the window. She knew they'd be covered when the Zamboni® dumped its load of snow.

Conclusion
Tony dug his skates out of the snow in time for the faceoff. The Minotaurs won, but Tony only tied Simon's record. After the game, Lorrisa confessed. Tony was just happy to have his skates back and didn't hold a grudge. He even promised to pass the puck more.

Case Solutions

The Case of the Angry Anchorman

(page 29)

Who stole Bull's wig?

• **Ursula Curtis.** Ursula was tired of her father working on the late news. She thought if she could get Max's mum in trouble, Bull would switch her shift with her father's and bring him back to the five o'clock news. Then Ursula would see more of him.

Where is the wig?

• It's in the rubbish bin, buried under the pile of paper napkins.

How did Max and Alison solve the case?

• Ursula was alone with Deb, Bull and the wig. She had the opportunity to steal it.
• Fran said the wig was gone when she walked into the dressing room. Ursula lied when she said the wig was on the stand when she left the make-up room.
• Ursula hid the wig under her zipped-up winter coat.
• Ursula complained about never seeing her father because he worked on the late news. That gave her a motive to get Bull mad at Max's mum.
• There wasn't a drop of juice on the table but Ursula said she made a big mess. She was lying to justify using so many paper napkins.

Conclusion

Ursula admitted to stealing the wig. She got the idea when she saw Bull get angry at Kyle. Bull pulled his wig out of the bin and read the five o'clock news. Ursula was not allowed to go on TV to present the charity money. The news went off without a hitch, except for when Bull O'Wiley sat in the large blob of bubble gum Kyle stuck on his TV studio seat. The joker was later heard saying, "Payback can be sticky, but it's always sweet."

The Case of the Missing Manga

(page 35)

Who stole Sarah's sketchbook?

• **Crystal Diallo.** Crystal wasn't interested in the Takahashi manga page. She wanted her drawing to be used for the cover of the school's comic book. With Sarah's drawing missing, hers would be used.

How did Max solve the case?

• Crystal said she didn't see anything because she was posing for photos with Sarah and Kengo Takahashi. But she left them to get a headband out of her bag, which was right beside Sarah's bag. That's when she grabbed Jake's sketchbook and made the switch.
• Crystal was lying about her mum being off work. Sarah's sketchbook was hidden in Crystal's bag and she wanted to get home before anyone saw it.

How? Why? Where?

Conclusion

Crystal admitted to switching the sketchbooks. She hoped that everyone would look for the manga page and not realise that Sarah's cover art was the real target. Crystal returned Sarah's sketchbook just in time to get Sarah's drawing on the cover of the comic. The comic was a hit, and Sarah agreed to use Crystal's drawing for the cover on the second issue.

The Case of the Elvis Prankster

(page 41)

Who is the Elvis prankster?

• **Chester Winfield.** Chester wanted to compete in the Grand Ballroom so badly that he dressed up like Elvis and pulled the pranks. He was hoping the Elvis convention would be blamed and get kicked out of the hotel, freeing the ballroom for the dog show.

How did Max solve the case?

• When Max and Eric talked to Chester, he was holding his dog in the white Elvis cape. That's why there was red hair on the cape in the hotel room.
• The chef said the sandwich buyer was a man, so it couldn't have been Nicole.
• Chester lied about who delivered the peanut butter sandwiches. The dog show woman said that Chester wasn't there when it happened. That's because he was disguised as Elvis delivering the sandwiches!
• Max heard Nicole giving Tinkerbell a bath just before the Elvis prankster got dressed. So she couldn't be the prankster.
• Witnesses saw an Elvis in a white cape pull the pranks – Alvin was wearing a black leather jacket. He couldn't be the prankster either.

Conclusion

Chester admitted to pulling the Elvis pranks. He was kicked out of the dog show and the Elvis competition went ahead as planned. Eric had a great performance and became the new Elvis champion.

Who? What? When?

The Case of the Gander River Grudge

(page 47)

Who is making the geese sick?

- **Kristen Taylor.** Kristen wanted the geese away from her flowers. She covered the river banks with soybeans because she knew the geese would all go there to eat the beans and leave her flowers alone.

How did Max solve the case?

- There were soybeans scattered in the back of Kristen's electric cart.
- Zack was using chemicals on the golf course, but Becca didn't find any chemicals on the soybeans, so Zack wasn't the culprit.
- Although he couldn't see who knocked him down, Max knew that it could not have been Zack because he was on the other side of the river. It also wasn't Josh or his dad because they were fishing under the bridge. That only left Kristen.
- Max heard a low hum right after he fell down the river bank. It was the sound of an electric cart. It was Kristen driving away after crashing into Max and Alison.

Conclusion

Kristen confessed to feeding soybeans to the geese. She didn't know that the beans would make the birds sick. They kept the geese away from her flowers and that's all that mattered to Kristen, so she kept spreading them along the river. She agreed to clean them off the banks and think of a safer way to keep the geese away from her flowers. The sick geese made a full recovery. Max wasn't so lucky. He broke his leg when Kristen knocked him down. Now he's got a cast on his leg and he's stuck at home.

The Case of the Nosy Neighbour

(page 53)

Did Russell rob the computer store?

No, but he was up to something sneaky. Although his parents told him not to have any friends over, Russell was planning to have a computer game party. Russell borrowed his friends' computers and was hooking them all up so they could play games together. Russell knew that Mrs Briggs was keeping an eye on him, so he snuck the computers into his house at night.

How did Alison solve the case?

- The van that Max saw did not match the description of the van caught on the computer store's surveillance camera.
- The stolen computers were brand new and still in their boxes, but the

computers Russell was unloading were older and used.

- The time on the grocery receipt was within a minute of the robbery at the computer store. Russell couldn't have stolen the computers and bought groceries at the same time.

Conclusion

Alison was able to calm Russell down before he gave Max another broken leg. The detectives apologised for spying on Russell. Mrs Briggs came out to see what all the fuss was about, and Russell admitted to planning a computer game party. Once the confusion was cleared up, Mrs Briggs let Russell have his computer game party, as long as she could supervise. Russell invited Max, Alison and Zoe over, and they had a great time playing computer games.

The Case of the Reflection Detection

(page 59)

Who is blinding the football players?

- **Kate Yoon.** Kate was mad that she had to quit the Meteors football team to work on her grades. She was so jealous of the other players that she didn't want to see them win the championships.
- She stood on her mountain bike and climbed onto the roofs of the toilets

and snack bar at the sports complex. From there, she used a mirror to reflect the bright sunlight into the eyes of the Meteor players to make them lose the game.

How did Max solve the case?

- The light flashes couldn't have come from the softball stands because the scoreboard blocked the view to the football field. The only clear shot was from the roof of the toilets.
- Kate said she didn't like football, but she was a former Meteors star player.
- Mr Huckle said he saw someone in blue shorts climb on a mountain bike to get on the roof of the toilets. That eliminated Lukas, who was wearing blue shorts but was riding a BMX bike.
- At the snack bar, Max couldn't see Kate but he could see her bike: it was leaning against the wall. He knew that she had just used it to climb onto the roof. She was hiding behind the snack bar's sign.

Conclusion

Max found Kate hiding on the roof of the snack bar. When she was confronted with the evidence, Kate admitted to distracting the players by bouncing sunlight off a mirror and into their eyes. The Meteors were able to come back from behind, thanks to some great goals from Alison and Andrea, and win the football championship.

Case Solutions

The Case of the Summer Sinker

(page 65)

Who is the real boat sinker?

- **Eugene Shaw.** Eugene lost his job at the marina because he went swimming with Warren. He was so mad that he decided to get back at Mr Klein, his old boss, by sinking the boats and putting the blame on Grandpa Santos.

How did Max solve the case?

- Eugene and Dan were wearing red baseball caps in the photo in Eugene's cabin. The cap in the boat must have belonged to Eugene because Dan lost his cap when the wind blew it off.
- The name inside the red cap was "Danny Santos." Grandpa Santos hated being called Danny, and Eugene was the only one who called him that. Eugene wrote the name in the cap and put it in the boat.
- Eugene told Dan that they'd watch the fireworks at his cabin, so that Dan would miss most of the show and not have an alibi for when the boat sinker struck.
- Eugene said that he saw the entire fireworks show, but he was lying. He left early because he said he wasn't feeling well.
- A witness said they saw a skinny kid in a red baseball cap moving along the marina during the fireworks. Grandpa Santos was a chubby kid.

Conclusion

When Max and Alison confronted him with the evidence, Eugene admitted to faking feeling sick during the fireworks, putting on the red baseball cap and sinking the boats. He apologised for blaming Dan and never telling the truth. When Warren saw the note he wrote to Eugene, he admitted that he was planning to get back at Dan, too. But after Warren rescued the boats, he wasn't mad at Grandpa Santos anymore. Warren, Eugene and Grandpa Santos were last seen laughing and sailing away on Trout Lake.

Square Search (page 16)

1. Leslie Chang **2.** Josh Spodek **3.** Max Finder **4.** Nanda Kanwar
5. Alison Santos **6.** Ethan Webster **7.** Zoe Palgrave **8.** Lukas Hajduk

Morse Message (page 22)

Max and Alison:
Thanks for solving the mystery of my crashed plane.
You really are the best detectives around. Thanks again.
Your friend,

Alex

Coach's Corner (page 28)

Tony DeMatteo is the Minotaurs'
leading scorer with 34 goals.
Lorrisa has scored 6 goals, **Alex**
has 17 goals, **Leslie** has 12 goals,
Josh has 6 goals and **Nicholas**
has 15 goals.

Decode It (page 40)

1. trip around the world
2. wish upon a star
3. top secret
4. horsing around
5. once in a blue moon
6. back-to-back victories
7. he came out of nowhere
8. double dutch
9. shop till you drop
10. green with envy

Photo Play (page 46)

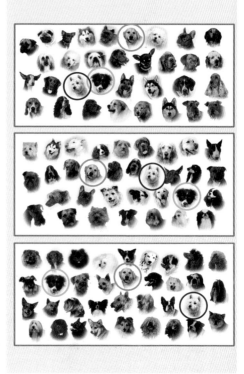

Cast Code (page 52)

Alison's message:
Max,
I guess detective work can be
a pain in the leg sometimes.
Alison

Max's message:
Alison,
Very funny. Those are the breaks
when you're a detective!
Max

What is it? (page 58)

1. helicopter

2. rubbish bin

3. line on road

4. garden hose

5. car

6. skateboard

7. basketball

8. cat

Forensics Quiz (page 64)

1. False — They are arch, loop and whorl.

2. True — They can also use things like palm prints,
footprints and bite marks.

3. True.

4. False — They often use clear tape.

5. True.

6. False — Strands of hair do not contain DNA.
But if scientists find a hair root they can
tell if the person is male or female.

7. True — A forensic vacuum can suck up things
like fibre, paint and glass.

8. True.

9. True.

10. False — But scientists are working on it.

Postcard Scramble

(page 72)

b

a

e

d

f

c

Max and Alison Come to Life

Peek into illustrator Michael Cho's sketchbook and see some of the first-ever drawings of Max and Alison.

My very first
MAX FINDER
DRAWING!
cho

My very first
ALISON SANTOS
DRAWING!
cho

MAX
FINDER

ALISON
SANTOS

Max & Alison
CHARACTER
STUDIES
&
ATTITUDES

cho

Max &
Alison

EDITOR'S NOTE:
notice how
the characters
changed over the
years.

MAX & ALISON   CHO

MAX FINDER   CHO

MAX FINDER   ALISON SANTOS   ETHAN   ZOE   BASHIR

Making a Mystery

A Max Finder Mystery graphic story goes through many stages before it's published. Every case starts off with writer Liam O'Donnell creating a detailed script. Liam outlines the plot, writes the captions and dialogue, as well as describes what the characters and setting look like. Michael Cho, the comic artist, creates the illustrations from this script.

Storyboarding

First, Michael draws quick sketches called thumbnails and decides how the panels will work together to tell the story.

Drawing Rough Sketches

Using the sketches as guides, Michael creates the illustrations for the story in blue pencil.

Revising Roughs

Sometimes the comic editor requests changes to the panels.

Revising Roughs

The illustrator draws the final artwork in black waterproof ink over the blue pencil drawings.

Colouring the Art

Michael gives guidelines for colouring to a colourist, an artist who specialises in colouring comics on a computer.

Publishing the Comic

After a designer adds the edited story onto the coloured art, the mystery is ready to be published.

MAX FINDER

Liam O'Donnell

Liam O'Donnell is the author of many children's books and the creator of *Max Finder Mystery* and the *Graphic Guide Adventures* series of graphic novels. In addition to writing for kids, Liam is a teacher, plays video games and goes camping (but not all at the same time). He lives in Toronto, Canada. You can visit him online at: **www.liamodonnell.com**.

Michael Cho

Michael Cho was born in Seoul, South Korea and moved to Canada when he was six years old. A graduate of the Ontario College of Art and Design, his distinctive drawings and comics have appeared in publications across North America. He is currently devoting his time to painting book covers, working on an art book of urban landscapes and creating more comics. You can always see his latest work online at: **www.michaelcho.com.**

Easy ways to use Max Finder in your classroom or library.

Readers' Theatre: Assign the different characters to pupils in your class and have them read their part aloud. The rest of the class can work together to solve the mystery.

Genre Study: What makes a mystery? Pupils can work in groups to research the elements of mysteries — clues, suspects, detectives, red herrings — and present their findings to the rest of the class.

DIY Mystery: Using the guide in *The Case of the Movie Set Mischief and Other Mysteries*, pupils can write and illustrate their own mini-mystery, then swap with a partner and try to solve someone else's creation.

Character Study: Have pupils study the roles (bully, snitch, prankster) that Max Finder characters play over a number of the mysteries and graph the results. Is there a pattern?

Comic Format Study: What makes a comic? Pupils can work in groups to research the conventions of comics — speech bubbles, caption boxes, panelled illustrations — and present their findings to the rest of the class.

See what people are saying about the series!

"In order to crack the cases, readers need to be observant and thoughtful and to have an eye for detail. In the absence of such qualities, however, I think that Max Finder Mystery may be an excellent tool to help young readers develop such traits."
— *Gregory Bryan, children's literature professor*

"Great for readers who enjoy mysteries in the vein of Encyclopedia Brown."
— *Booklist*

"In addition to appealing to amateur sleuths, these graphic mysteries offer reluctant readers short, manageable reads within an inviting comic-book format."
— *Quill & Quire*

"If you have a youngster who enjoys the graphic novel format and loves a good mystery, they'll love these Max Finder mysteries!"
— *D. Fowler, online reviewer*

Max Finder Mysteries
— *Association of Educational Publishers' Award, Graphic Novel category, Winner*